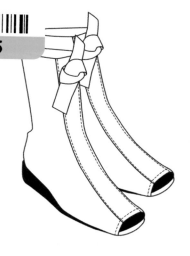

# 1960s Fashion to Colour

Illustrated and designed by Antonia Miller

Additional illustration by Simona Bursi

Written by Emily Bone and Abigail Wheatley

Historical fashion expert: Jemima Klenk

## Usborne Quicklinks

For links to websites to find out more about 1960s fashion, go to the Usborne Quicklinks website at www.usborne.com/quicklinks and type in the title of this book. Please read our internet safety guidelines at the Usborne Quicklinks website.

# Sixties style

The sixties saw a fashion revolution. Many designers threw out the old, safe, restrictive women's fashions of the 1950s and instead experimented with daring innovations, such as short skirts, 'bobbed' haircuts and new fashion materials such as plastic and synthetic fabrics. Even for men, fashions changed radically, with flared trousers, bold prints and textures and different, longer hairstyles.

Sixties fashion celebrated a youthful, casual look, defined by A-line minidresses and miniskirts in bright colours.

Art had a big influence on fashion. These fabrics are based on a style of art known as 'op art'.

Different looks developed for those with different musical tastes. Some rock and pop music generated a look based on mixing modern fashions with vintage clothes, using bold prints and colours.

Through most of the sixties, heels tended to be medium to low, and flat shoes and boots became a key look.

Accessories were bold and chunky, often in affordable materials such as plastic.

For formal occasions, tailoring often skimmed the body to give a straight silhouette. Hats and gloves were considered essential.

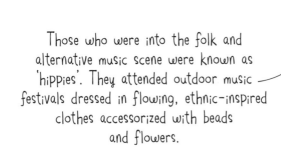

Those who were into the folk and alternative music scene were known as 'hippies'. They attended outdoor music festivals dressed in flowing, ethnic-inspired clothes accessorized with beads and flowers.

Long hair and elaborate updos were popular, but sleek, short haircuts also came into fashion.

These 'bobbed' styles were created by celebrated sixties hairdresser Vidal Sassoon.

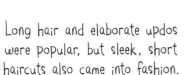

# Mods

In the early sixties, some teenagers began to dress in stylish, understated clothes. The were known as 'mods', short for 'modernist.'

Mods often came together in groups. Members of the same group wore the same badge or patch on their coats.

Union jack patch

Royal Air Force 'roundel' badge

Black, white, and muted shades such as grey and navy, were characteristic mod colours.

This jacket is styled to look like a man's suit jacket.

Flat pumps

Trilby hat

Sunglasses were a must-have mod accessory.

You could colour this car coat in shades inspired by the fabric swatches on the left.

Leather miniskirt

# Office wear

Office workers had to look smart and presentable. Women often wore a suit consisting of a dress or skirt paired with a tailored jacket.

The yoke of this dress is made from swirly patterned fabric.

Strings of pearls were popular accessories for wearing with a suit.

Women wore tights or stockings, often in pale brownish shades.

Wool fabrics in bright block colours, or classic patterns such as this hound's tooth check, were often used for suits.

Pillbox
hat

Men always
wore a suit and
tie to the office.

Leave the
gloves white.

You could colour
the main part of
this outfit in a bold
colour and make the
stripes and belt a
darker shade.

# Swimwear

Swimwear designs were revolutionized during the sixties by the use of modern, stretchy fabrics and the surge in popularity of two-piece swimsuits such as the bikini.

This outfit features swim shorts and a vest-style top.

Headscarf

Beach bag

Flat sandals were a practical beach or poolside option.

Elastene bikini
with ruffles

Strapless elastene
bandeau bikini top

A new, stretchy fabric
called elastene was
invented in 1959. It kept
its shape while wet, so it
was great for swimwear.

Tie-side elastene bikini bottoms

Colour this
bikini top, shirt
and trousers
to match.

# Swinging London

Beret

During the sixties, London became a creative hub for pop music, fashion and design. It was nicknamed 'swinging London' - meaning hip or fashionable.

London-based fashion designer Mary Quant designed minidresses like this one, using stretchy fabrics in bright colours.

Knee-high socks were a popular look.

You could add a pattern, such as flowers or polka dots, to this minidress.

Pixie cut

5-pointed bob

Vidal Sassoon, a famous hairdresser, created these iconic sixties hairstyles in his London salon.

Colour these knee-high boots in a bright shade.

Union Jack shopping bag

Coloured ankle boots worn over white tights

# Space age

The Sixties saw many firsts of space exploration, from the first person to enter space in 1961 to the first astronauts to land on the Moon in 1969. This fascination with space was reflected in fashion design.

'Goggle' sunglasses were inspired by the visors on astronauts' helmets.

Space also influenced furniture design. Perspex 'bubble chairs' made the sitter feel weightless, as if floating in space.

Geometric shapes and bold colours gave clothes a futuristic look.

Hats echoed the shapes of astronauts' helmets.

You could colour these outfits in metallic, space-age colours.

Clothes made of plastic gave a feel similar to shiny space suits.

Rubber boots based on those worn by atronauts

# Formal dresses

Dresses for formal occasions such as dances, dinners and weddings were modestly cut. Women often wore long gloves, too.

Later, dresses with flared, 'A-line' skirts came into fashion.

In the early sities, full skirts were a key look.

Gown with long sleeves and a jewelled belt clasp

Two-piece evening outfit with a fitted bodice and a gathered skirt

Luxurious fabrics such as silk, brocade and lace were often used.

You could add patterns inspired by these swatches to the dresses on this page.

Evening shoes with pointed toes

# Pop and op

Some fashions were based on modern art styles popular in the 1960s, such as 'op art' and 'pop art'.

Art-inspired accessories were bold and blocky.

Pop art inspired fabrics like this, using bright colours and repeating shapes

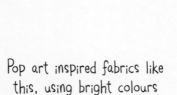

This fabric creates an optical illusion – the idea behind op art.

A-line minidress

You could colour this dress in bold shades inspired by the fabric swatch on the left.

Colour some parts of the dress in bright, primary shades. Leave other parts white.

Colour the ankle boots to match the dress.

# Casual wear

Many women welcomed the arrival of new fashions and fabrics that enabled them to dress in comfortable, casual clothes.

Polo neck jumper

Fabric swatches to inspire your colouring

A-line miniskirt

Slim-fitting 'drainpipe' trousers were popular throughout the sixties as part of a casual look.

Soft felt
hat

Stretchy
cotton jersey
top

Colour this knitted
minidress in blocks of
different bright colours.

Jeans were an
essential part of
women's wardrobes
for the first time.

Tights became
widely available as
a comfortable and
practical option to wear
under short skirts.

Flat
Pumps

# Paper and plastic

Sixties fashion designers liked to experiment with fabrics such as paper, and a type of plastic known as PVC (polyvinyl chloride), that weren't traditionally used for clothes.

PVC was originally used for pipes and electrical cables, before fashion designers started to use it.

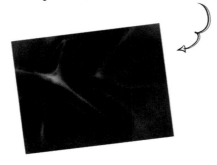

Plastic could be hot to wear, but holes could be punched in it to make it cooler.

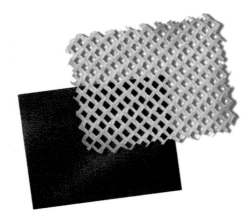

Paper and plastic contrasted well with natural fabrics, such as wool.

PVC came in many shades – even transparent. Its shiny surface and stiff texture made it great for structured clothes such as this raincoat.

Knee-high socks

Cheap paper dresses were intended to be worn once, then thrown away.

Some paper dresses had photographs printed onto them.

Colour this geometric patterned paper dress in bold, bright colours.

Shiny PVC trousers

# Outer wear

For formal occasions, women wore coats with gloves and a hat or headscarf. Going without a hat was considered more casual.

Fitted wool coat with contrasting cross design

This type of loosely tailored coat was made popular in the early sixties by fashion icons such as Jackie Kennedy, the wife of the American President.

You could colour each quarter of this coat a different colour.

Peaked
'helmet' hat

Double-breasted
checked wool
car coat

High collar

This style of cape
was known as
'swing' because of
the way the fabric
moved. Swing coats
were also popular.

Colour this coat
in muted shades
suitable for mods
(see pages 4-5).

Knee-length
boots

# Accessories

'Mod' style sunglasses

'Pop art' style earrings

Plastic flower ring

Hat with side button detail

Lace-up mid-heel shoes

Leather bag with a geometric design

Bag with snap fastener

Square sunglasses

'Flower power' brooch

Colour these court shoes in bright block colours.

Soft fabric handbag

Stripy plastic ring

Bag with bamboo handle

Two-tone slingback loafers

Plastic brooch

Pointed 'winklepicker' shoes

You could colour these flowers orange.

Round evening bag

Felt hat with ribbon band

Sunglasses with a ray pattern

Fabric bag with a swirly pattern

Dangly plastic earrings

Chisel-toe boots

# Flamboyant fashion

In the late sixties, fashion designers experimented with extravagant, eye-catching shapes, patterns and textures, often combining new and vintage clothes to create an individual look.

Colour this dress in bright colours such as lime green, shocking pink, tangerine and purple.

This 'peacock' dress, with a very wide, flaring skirt, echoed the shape of a peacock's tail.

Floral-print
velvet jacket

Suede boots

Vintage,
military-style
jacket

Bright,
striped
trousers

# Music festival

From 1967, rock and pop music festivals held in huge outdoor venues became increasingly popular.

Feather earrings

Festival-goers, who were often known as 'hippies', wore ethnic-inspired clothes and grew their hair long.

Denim shirt with patterned fabric patches

Fringed leather bag

Loose coat worn over a flowing maxi dress

Moccassin boots

'Afghan' jacket worn over a tie-dyed top

Kaftan dress inspired by loose robes from North Africa and the Middle East

Flared trousers were an essential fashion item for both men and women from the mid-sixties.

# End of an era

At the end of the sixties, fashions were on the move again. Skirts were longer, flares were wider, and women often tied back their hair with scarves or turbans.

Bold, floral prints were combined with geometric patterns in striking colours.

Maxi dress

Headscarf

Flared trousers with a low 'hipster' waistband

Some fashions of the late sixties looked back to previous decades. For example, this jumpsuit echoed a look popular in the 1930s.

Use this fabric swatch to help you when choosing colours for the jumpsuit.

Safari suits like this one usually came in pale shades such as beige or light blue.

Wide-leg jumpsuit

Toe-post sandals

# Nightwear

Sixties nightwear followed the fashion trends, using modern fabrics and shapes similar to daywear.

Ruffle-trimmed pyjama top

Add a floral pattern if you like.

Cropped pyjama pants

Floral print A-line nylon dressing gown

Mules with a rosette trim